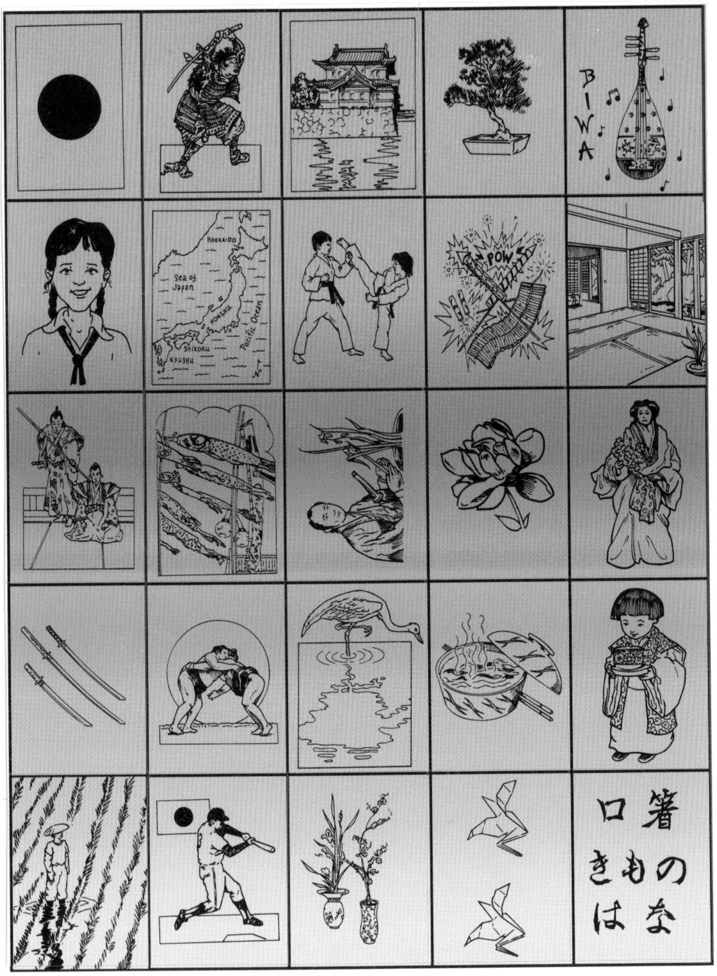
BIWA
HOKKAIDO
Sea of Japan
HONSHU
Pacific Ocean
SHIKOKU
KYUSHU
POW
口 箸
きもの
はな

HOKKAIDO
Sea of Japan
HONSHU
Pacific Ocean
SHIKOKU
KYUSHU
POW
口 箸
きもの
はな

BIWA
HOKKAIDO
Sea of Japan
HONSHU
Pacific Ocean
SHIKOKU
KYUSHU
POW
口 箸
きもの
はな

BIWA
HOKKAIDO
Sea of Japan
HONSHU
Pacific Ocean
SHIKOKU
KYUSHU
POW
口 箸
きもの
はな

# JAPAN

**By**
**Jane Pofahl**

Cover Illustration by
Mark Anthony

Inside Illustrations by
Marc F. Johnson

*Publishers*
Instructional Fair • TS Denison
Grand Rapids, Michigan 49504

**Credits**
Author: Jane Pofahl
Cover Artist: Mark Anthony
Inside Illustrations: Marc F. Johnson
Project Director.Editor: Danielle de Gregory
Art Production: Darcy Bell-Myers
Typesetting: Deborah McNiff

**About the Author**
    Jane Pofahl has taught kindergarten through the eighth grade in Minnesota schools. She has worked with students outside the classroom as school yearbook and newspaper editor, play director, speech coach, and private tutor. Her biography has appeared three times in *Who's Who in American Education*.
    Jane Pofahl lives in Apple Valley, Minnesota, with her husband, Don, and Buddy, the Wonder Dog.

Standard Book Number: 513-02380-1
*Japan*
Copyright © 1996 by Instructional Fair • TS Denison
2400 Turner Avenue NW
Grand Rapids, Michigan 49504

# Introduction

History is the living record of the human race—exciting as it is varied. *The Time Traveler Series* will aid you as you teach the colorful history and culture of countries around the world to your students. Explore such topics as geography, city and rural living, art and music, historic events, holidays, famous cities, and meet the historic personalities who helped shape the cultures of countries today.

After each topic is presented, activity pages are provided for your students to implement suggested vocabulary, conduct further research, and provide creative answers/solutions to historical situations. Fun reproducible pages are also included to review the historical and cultural facts studied on the preceding pages.

Each book contains the following:

- topic information pages
- research/activity pages (including maps, charts, research topics, and creative thinking activities)
- reproducible activity pages
- cultural stickers

*The Time Traveler Series* was created to spark the sense of intrigue in your students and lay a foundation for enjoyable history instruction and learning. Have fun!

# Table of Contents

# The History of Japan

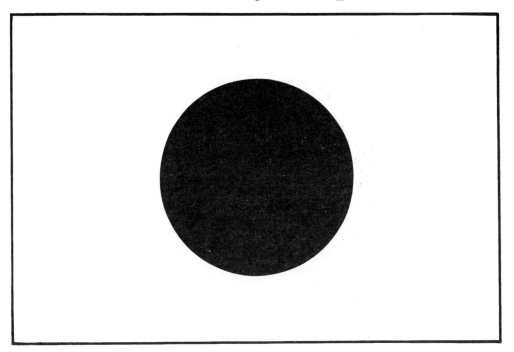

Japan is made up of four main islands, thousands of smaller islands, and is located east of Korea in the Pacific Ocean. There are over 124 million people living on the Japanese islands. The Japanese call their country *Nippon,* which means "source of the sun."

Japan is a democracy, but also has an emperor. Just as in Great Britain, the emperor is a monarch who has no political power. However, the emperor is respected and symbolizes the head of the nation to the Japanese.

Historians believe that the first settlers in Japan came in boats from China, Korea, and Manchuria. The oldest race still living in Japan is the Ainu, who live mainly on Hokkaido today.

The early Japanese lived together in clans; they fought each other to determine the ruling clan. By A.D. 400, the Yamato clan had become the rulers on Kyushu and had begun the dynasty that still reigns in Japan.

The Golden Age of Japan occurred from 794 to 1185. It was known as the *Heian Period* because the capital was moved from Nara to Heian, which was later renamed Kyoto. During this time, Japanese art, music, calligraphy, and writing flourished. It was also a time of great unrest, and a warrior named Minamoto became the first *shogun*, or ruling military dictator, in 1192. The Bushido Code of Loyalty and Service was formed and followed by *samurai* warriors at this time also.

In 1274 and in 1281, Mongol leader Kublai Khan tried to invade Japan. Both attempts failed.

Life in Japan was changed forever in 1543 when Portuguese traders arrived and introduced firearms to the Japanese. Soon traders from Spain, England, and the Netherlands had brought missionaries to Japan to convert the Japanese from Buddhism to Christianity. The Japanese government tried to stop the influence of Westerners in 1637 by ordering all foreigners to leave Japan and closing the country to the world. Japan was isolated from the world for the next two hundred years.

In 1853, Commander Matthew Perry of the United States convinced the Japanese government to allow trade between the two nations. The Japanese also agreed to trade with Great Britain, the Netherlands, and Russia by 1858.

In 1867, the ruling *shogun* family was defeated by Emperor Meiji, ending the rule of *shoguns* and the power of the *samurai*. Emperor Meiji moved the capital from Kyoto to Edo, which he renamed Tokyo. The emperor also set up a modern army and navy, ordered all Japanese children to attend school, and encouraged the growth of new businesses. By 1900, Japan was a modern, powerful nation.

Japan fought in World War II from 1940 to 1945. Hostilities between Japan and the United States grew and erupted into warfare in 1941 when Japan attacked Pearl Harbor Naval Base in Hawaii, precipitating the entry of the United States in World War II. When Hiroshima and Nagasaki were atom-bombed by the United States in 1945, the Emperor of Japan surrendered to the United States and World War II ended. Under American occupation until 1952, Japan became a democracy in 1947.

Since World War II, the hard-working Japanese people have rebuilt their nation into a prosperous democracy where ninety-nine percent of the population can read and write. Japan is the world's largest producer of automobiles, televisions, and video cassette recorders.

# The Geography of Japan

Japan is an island nation. It is surrounded by the Pacific Ocean to the east, the Philippine and East China Seas in the south, the Sea of Okhotsk to the north, and the Sea of Japan to the west.

The climate of Japan is affected by two ocean currents. The eastern coast of Honshu is warmed by the Japan current flowing northward from the Philippines. The Oyashio current flowing southward from Siberia cools the eastern coast of Hokkaido.

The country of Japan includes thousands of small islands. The four main islands hold almost all of Japan's land area. The main islands include Honshu, Hokkaido, Kyushu, and Shikoku.

Honshu is Japan's largest island and has an area of 87,805 square miles (227,414 square kilometers). It contains many of Japan's larger cities and eighty percent of Japan's population. Ten mountain ranges coexist on Honshu. The Japan Alps, Japan's highest mountains, are located in central Honshu. Mount Fuji is Japan's tallest and most famous peak—an inactive volcano on Honshu. The Kanto Plain to the east is a major farming and business region, and holds the capital city of Tokyo. Other major cities on Honshu include Yokohama, Osaka, and Kyoto.

Hokkaido is the island farthest north. It has primarily forested mountains and hills. The climate is very cold, and the heavy snowfalls make Hokkaido a popular island for winter sports. The main city on Hokkaido is Sapporo.

Kyusku is Japan's most southern main island. It holds about eleven percent of the total population. Forested mountains run down the center of Kyusku. Cities are located in the northwestern section of the island, which has rolling hills and plains. Kyushu's major city is Nagasaki.

Shikoku is the smallest of Japan's main islands. The Shikoku Mountains cross the island from east to west. A bridge has been built to link Shikoku to Hiroshima on Honshu. Shikoku's largest city is Matsuyama.

# The Geography of Japan

## RESEARCH QUESTIONS

1. Define the following vocabulary words: *climate, current, coexist*, and *primarily*.

2. Make a weather map of Japan for January and August.

3. Choose one of the four main Japanese islands: Honshu, Hokkaido, Kyushu, or Shikoku. Research the island and explain your findings in an informative speech using at least three visual aids. (This would make an excellent group project as well.)

## PROJECTS

1. Make a three-dimensional map of the Japanese islands. Include mountain ranges and major cities.

2. Make a model of Japan's highest peak, Mount Fuji. Include a written paragraph of facts about Mount Fuji.

3. Japan is known as the "Land of the Rising Sun." Why do you think this is so?

4. Using either cloth or construction paper, make the flag of Japan. What does the symbolism on the flag mean?

# The Map of Japan

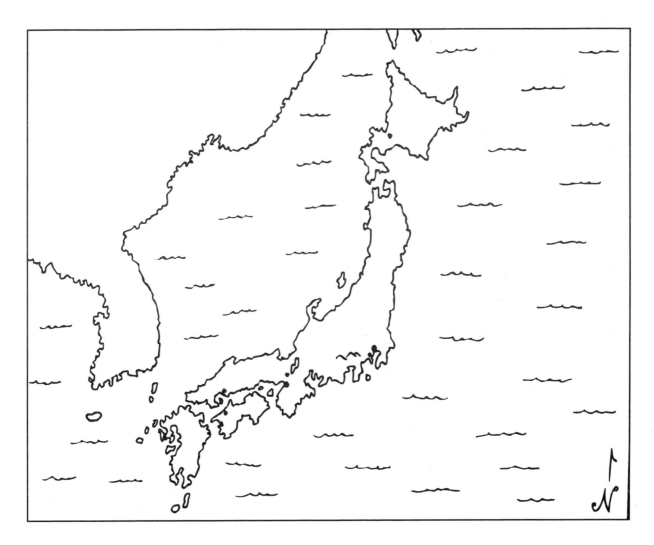

1. Using a world atlas, locate the following on the map above.
   - Hokkaido
   - Honshu
   - Shikoku
   - Kyushu
   - Tokyo
   - Sapporo
   - Osaka
   - Yokohama
   - Kyoto
   - Hiroshima
   - Nagasaki
   - Matsuyama
   - Mount Fuji
   - Japan Alps
   - Sea of Japan
   - Pacific Ocean

2. Japan has four main islands and _____ of smaller islands.

3. In January, the weather in Sapporo would be _____

   _____

4. In August, the weather in Nagasaki would be_____

   _____

# Samurai Warriors

*"The sword is the soul of the samurai." Tokugawa Ieyasu*

The word *samurai* means "those who serve." The *samurai* warriors of ancient Japan did indeed serve their masters—often at the cost of their own lives.

*Samurai* warriors were organized around A.D. 1000. The ruling military dictator, called the *shogun*, commanded his overseers, known as *daimyos*, to gather a band of elite soldiers whose sole purpose would be to protect their *daimyos*, and if necessary, the *shogun* himself. As time went by, the *samurai* developed into a warrior class that was feared and respected throughout the empire. About ten percent of the population were *samurai* warriors. The title of *samurai* was passed down from generation to generation.

*Samurai* wore two swords, one long and the other short. A *samurai's* armor consisted of a helmet, a metal-clad shirt that covered his arms and torso, and metal leg guards. As the *samurai* began to lose power in Japan, they tried to maintain the respect of the people by wearing more and more elaborate uniforms, which were really for show and not for fighting.

A code of loyalty, called Bushido, tied the *samurai* to their *daimyos*. According to the code of Bushido, or "Way of the Warrior," a *samurai* would obey his lord's orders without question, even if it meant his own death. A *samurai* would not profit from any battle. He had to practice his martial arts skills constantly. A *samurai* did not bring disgrace to his family or lord, and maintained a good reputation. He would defend to the death his honor and the honor of his lord.

The code of bushido is seen in one of Japan's more famous tales, remembered as "The Forty-Seven Ronin of Ako." Two *daimyos*, named Kira and Asano, had a disagreement. Kira embarrassed Asano in public, and Asano drew his sword on Kira. Losing control in public was as bad as losing respect. Asano was banished for his action, and committed *hara-kari*, a ritual form of suicide. Asano's *samurai* were then lordless, or "ronin." The forty-seven ronin watched Kira for two years, then avenged the honor of their dead lord by killing Kira. The forty-seven turned themselves into the authorities, who admired the loyalty of the ronin but could not excuse their actions. The ronin were ordered to commit *hara-kari*, which they did. Their tombs are at the Segaku-ji Temple in Tokyo.

The *samurai* warriors lost all their power when Emperor Menji defeated the last *shogun* in 1876 and ordered all *samurai* warriors to turn over their swords to the emperor's men.

# Samurai Warriors

### RESEARCH QUESTIONS

1. Define the following vocabulary words: *samurai, shogun, daimyo, elite, sole, torso, elaborate, Bushido, martial, reputation, hara-kari,* and *ronin.*

2. The martial arts of *judo* and *karate* were practiced by the *samurai* to sharpen their fighting skills. Research *judo* and *karate.* Share your information with the class in a demonstration speech.

3. Find out about the lives of two men important to the history of the *samurai.* Research either *Yoritomo Minamoto* or *Tokugawa Ieyasu.* Present your findings in a two-page report using at least two visual aids.

4. What exactly happened to the *samurai*? How did their way of life come to an end? Research the end of the *samurai,* and present your information to the group as if you were a reporter on a television news special report.

### PROJECTS

1. Make a chart comparing the Japanese *samurai* warriors with the knights in Europe.

2. Create a feudal pyramid for Japan showing the most powerful to the least.

3. Using resource books, draw a *samurai* in full dress armor.

4. Each *samurai* family had a flag for identification, much like the coats-of-arms worn by knights in the Middle Ages. Design a flag for your family.

5. Write your own code of Bushido. (This is also an excellent group or class project.)

6. For the teacher: For more background on the *shogun* system and the *samurai,* watch the videos *The Seven Samurai* and *Shogun.*

# Samurai Savvy

So you think you know all about the legendary *samurai* warriors of ancient Japan? Let's see just how savvy you are about the *samurai*.

Read each statement. If it is correct, write TRUE in the blank. If the statement is incorrect, write FALSE in the blank.

_____ 1. A *samurai* warrior would follow his master's commands, even if it meant the *samurai* could die.

_____ 2. A *samurai* would use his sword only when there were no other knives in the house.

_____ 3. To learn inner discipline, the *samurai* studied the art of flower arranging.

_____ 4. The *samurai* preferred *noh* theater to *Kabuki* theater.

_____ 5. The *samurai* felt that they were the greatest warriors in all Japan, so they did not need to practice their martial arts skills once they had proven themselves in battle.

_____ 6. The samurai became wealthy from all of the gold and riches they received after they defeated the *shogun's* enemies.

_____ 7. The code of loyalty followed by the samurai was called *Bushido,* meaning "The Way of the Worthy."

_____ 8. To lose the respect of others was worse than death to a *samurai*.

_____ 9. The title of *samurai* was passed down from father to son.

_____ 10. The *samurai* warriors were disbanded by Emperor Menji in 1876.

# City Life, Rural Life

Four-fifths of the population of Japan live in cities. Japan's four main cities of Tokyo, Yokohama, Osaka, and Nagoya are located on Honshu. These large cities resemble Western cities with concrete and steel office buildings, rush hour traffic jams, and a variety of stores, restaurants, and theaters.

Many Japanese living in cities work in banks, hotels, businesses, or government jobs. Japan has a low unemployment rate. There are some poor neighborhoods in Japan, but very few slums.

Education is a high priority in Japan. All Japanese children go to school through the ninth grade. After that they must pass a test to continue into senior high. For advanced schooling, there are junior and technical colleges as well as universities in Japan.

Japanese city dwellers live in modern apartment buildings and traditional Japanese houses. A traditional house is a simple one- or two-story building made of wood with a sloping, tiled roof. Rooms are separated by sliding paper screens called *shoji*. During the day, people sit on *tatami,* reed mats, instead of chairs and eat their meals at low tables using chopsticks. At night, the reed mats are put away and padded quilts, called *futons*, are spread on the floor for sleeping. Every home includes an alcove, called a *tokonoma*, decorated with a hanging scroll and a simple flower arrangement on a small table.

Japan's big cities face serious problems of housing shortages and air and water pollution. The crime rate in Japan is low, however, so people feel safe to walk the streets during the day or night.

Most of Japan's rural population live and work on family-owned farms. Others live along the seacoast and make their living by fishing and harvesting edible seaweed. Many rural families live in traditional wooden houses, having one to four rooms. People living in rural areas do not make as much money as those in the cities do, but rural dwellers do own cars, television sets, and modern appliances to help make their lives comfortable.

Since the 1950s, many Japanese have moved to the cities to find work in businesses and factories. Family farms are run by older men and women while their children seek new lives in the big cities.

# City Life, Rural Life

## RESEARCH QUESTIONS

1. Define the following vocabulary words: *population, unemployment, traditional, story* (in a building), *shoji, tatami, futon, tokonoma, harvesting, edible, appliance,* and *dweller*.

2. Draw a map of the island of Honshu. Locate the cities of Tokyo, Yokohama, Osaka, and Nagoya.

3. Choose one of the large cities mentioned in the article: Tokyo, Yokohama, Osaka, or Nagoya. Find out more about that city. Present your findings in a two-page report using at least two visual aids.

## PROJECTS

1. Using a recipe, prepare a dish of edible seaweed. Eat it and compare the taste and texture with foods found in the West.

2. Make a chart showing the differences between a traditional Japanese home and an American home.

3. A majority of women in Japan attend junior colleges and technical schools, while many of the men go to colleges and universities. Why do you think this is so?

4. Your parents have a large farm on Honshu. All of your siblings have left for the big cities. You would like to live and work in Tokyo with the rest of your friends, but there is no one else to take over the farm. What will you do?

# Tokyo

Tokyo is the capital of Japan. It is located on the southern shore of the island of Honshu. It sits on the Kanto Plain along Tokyo Bay. Many rivers flow into Tokyo Bay, including the Sumida, Arakawa, Edogawa, and the Tama. Tokyo is the second largest city in the world.

Japan is a land of earthquakes and typhoons. The Great Kanto earthquake of 1923 destroyed large sections of Tokyo. Sixty thousand people died from the earthquake and the fires afterward. Typhoons also present a danger to the Japanese. Large dikes have been built near Tokyo Bay to prevent the large-scale flooding caused by typhoons.

Japan's capital city began as a small fishing village named Edo. The city was founded in the 1590s when a *shogun* named Ieyasu built a magnificent castle at Edo. The city was renamed in 1867 when Emperor Meiji moved his capital to Edo and changed its name to Tokyo, meaning "Eastern Capital."

If you visit Tokyo in early April, you will see its famous cherry blossoms in bloom. In summer, you can see lotus blossoms on display at Ueno Park, which also includes Tokyo's largest concert hall, several museums and art galleries, a zoo, a temple and shrine, and the tombs of Japanese rulers. Foreign tourists and Japanese visitors alike pay a visit to the impressive Meiji Shrine when they are in Tokyo.

The Imperial Palace, where the Emperor lives, is built on the ruins of Edo Castle. Visitors are allowed to view the palace only on January 2 for New Year's and on the Emperor's birthday, December 23. However, there are gardens, art galleries, and the National Theater located on the palace grounds which you can visit.

You may choose between three amusement parks in Tokyo. The Korakuen features a giant roller coaster and a train that does the loop. Toshima-en Amusement Park is much larger with four roller coasters, haunted houses, and seven swimming pools. The most popular park in Tokyo is Micky Mouse's favorite—Tokyo Disneyland!

As a major city, Tokyo has its share of problems with providing adequate housing for its citizens and water and air pollution problems. However, its crime rate is much lower than other large cities in the West, such as New York or London, making it one of the safest large cities in the world.

# Tokyo

## RESEARCH QUESTIONS

1. Define the following vocabulary words: *typhoon, dike, magnificent, impressive, shrine,* and *amusement.*

2. Write a weather report for Tokyo for June 15th and for August 15th.

3. How tall is Tokyo Tower? For what is it used? Find out and report your information to the class.

4. Make a chart showing the world's five largest cities in order of population size.

## PROJECTS

1. Seven percent of Japan's total population live in Tokyo. Why do you think that is so?

2. Make a model of the *Meiji Shrine.*

3. The 1964 Summer Olympic Games were held in Tokyo. You were there as a competitor. Tell the class what sport you competed and how well you performed.

4. If you only had one day to spend in Tokyo, would you rather visit Ueno Park, Korakuen Park, Toshima-en Park, or Tokyo Disneyland? Give at least three reasons for your answer.

# Tokyo Crossword

## ACROSS

6. Visitors are allowed to view this only twice a year.
7. The place of honor built to remember the great Emperor Meiji
9. Many rivers in Japan flow into this body of water.
10. The original name for the city of Tokyo
11. The meaning of the word Tokyo
13. The location of a concert hall, art galleries, a zoo, a temple, and a shrine in Tokyo
14. It is difficult to provide adequate _ _ _ _ _ _ _ for all of Tokyo's citizens.

## DOWN

1. This is low in Tokyo, making it one of the world's safest large cities.
2. The emperor of Japan's birthday is on the twenty-third of this month.
3. Edo started out as a small _ _ _ _ _ _ _ _ _ _ _ _ _.
4. The *shogun* who built Edo Castle
5. Nation made up of four large islands and thousands of small islands
8. Capital city of Japan
10. Responsible for killing sixty thousand Japanese in Tokyo in 1923
12. Island on which Tokyo is located

17

# Daily Life in Japan

Japanese people have learned to be disciplined, in part due to their physical environment. The cold winters in the north, the hot summers in the south, and the typhoons, earthquakes, and volcanoes on the islands have taught the Japanese to be flexible and ready to adapt to changes.

Japanese clothing is one change the people have seen over the years. Traditional dress for men and women was a *kimono*, a one-piece wraparound garment held in place at the waist by a sash. Although many Japanese choose to wear western styles of clothing today, people often wear *kimonos* at home and on special occasions.

The Japanese language can be very difficult to write. It was developed from the Chinese system of character writing, or *kanji*. Using *kanji* as a model, the Japanese developed two separate alphabets called *hiragana* and *katakana*. There are more than 60,000 *kanji* characters, but the majority of books and newspapers use only 1,850 *kanji*, which is the same number that high school seniors are expected to know. Traditionally, Japanese is written from top to bottom, beginning at the right-hand side of the page. Today, text in books appears from left to right in Japan, as it is in the West. The art of beautiful handwriting, known as calligraphy, is taught in school to children who learn to write Japanese characters using a brush and black ink.

Food is celebrated in Japan not only for how it tastes, but also how it looks. Each item is arranged artistically on the plate so that it pleases the eye. Rice is the staple food for Japan and is eaten at every meal. Fish and tofu are the main sources of protein in Japan, whether eaten raw or cooked. Vegetables are popular and green tea is a favorite beverage.

Japanese people work hard, but they also know how to enjoy themselves. Gardening and working on handicrafts or hobbies are the most popular leisure activities in Japan. The emphasis in sports is on physical fitness, some of the more popular sports are jogging, baseball, swimming, golf, and cycling. Skiing and ice skating are favorite pastimes on Hokkaido. The number-one spectator sport in Japan is *sumo* wrestling, in which two three-hundred pound wrestlers attempt to throw their opponent outside of a ring of straw. Many Japanese enjoy the sport of *kendo*, a form of fencing in which two opponents use bamboo poles instead of swords. The martial arts of *judo* and *karate* are also practiced to teach self-discipline and self-defense.

# Daily Life in Japan

## RESEARCH QUESTIONS

1. Define the following vocabulary words: *discipline, typhoon, flexible, traditional, kanji, calligraphy, artistically, staple, protein, tofu, beverage, handicrafts, leisure, emphasis, participate, spectator, kendo, martial, judo,* and *karate.*

2. Find out about the marriage customs of Japan. Present your findings to the class in the form of a skit.

3. Research the history of *calligraphy.* Present an oral report to the class on your information, and try to locate someone in your community who would demonstrate *calligraphy* for the class.

4. Choose one of the traditional Japanese sports mentioned in the article: *sumo wrestling, kendo, kudo,* or *karate.* Write a two-page report, including at least two visual aids.

mouth        chopstick

kimono

flower

## PROJECTS

1. Make your own *kimono*! Write to Folkwear Patterns, Box 3798, San Rafael, California 94902, for more information.

2. Do you have a yen for *yen*? Find out how the Japanese *yen* compares with the United States dollar.

3. Learn to count from one to ten in Japanese.

4. Find a book on how to do *calligraphy*, then write an original poem in *calligraphy*.

5. Write a menu of a typical Japanese meal for four people.

# Chestnuts Cooked in Green Tea

Children of all ages in Japan enjoy this tasty snack!

> 6 peeled chestnuts
> 1 tablespoon green tea leaves
> 5 teaspoons sugar
> 1 teaspoon soy sauce

With a small, sharp knife, cut a long gash in the flat, softer side of each of the chestnuts. Put the chestnuts in a 1-quart saucepan, cover them completely with cold water, and bring to a boil. Cook briskly for 2 or 3 minutes, then remove the chestnuts from the pan and peel off the shells when cool enough to touch.

Using the same saucepan, cover the chestnuts with cold water and the tea leaves and bring to a boil. Lower the heat and simmer uncovered for 20 minutes, or until the chestnuts show no resistance when pierced with the tip of a sharp knife. Drain and wash under cold running water. Leave the brown membrane intact.

Combine 1 cup cold water, the sugar, and the chestnuts in a saucepan and bring to a boil. Reduce the heat and simmer 20 minutes, then stir in the soy sauce. Simmer another 5 minutes, remove from the heat, and cool to room temperature before draining and serving.

# Festivals in Japan

The Japanese are a disciplined people who allow themselves to relax and have fun during many festivals throughout the year. Some *matsuri*, or festivals, are religious and some are based on ancient folklore.

A major holiday celebrated on all the Japanese islands is the seven-day New Year's festival. On January 1, three bamboo and pine branches are placed on each door for good luck in the coming year, and families and friends enjoy seafood, rice cakes, and spiced *saki* wine. Many people dress in traditional *kimonos* and visit shrines on this day. On January 2, people write their first poems, sing their first songs, and gather special treasures around them so that their first dreams in the new year will be happy ones. Children fly brightly colored kites. The festival ends on January 7 when traditional rice porridge is eaten.

On March 3 *Hinamatsuri*, the Festival of Dolls, is celebrated. It is also known as Girls' Day; and girls dress in their finest *kimonos* and are allowed to play with the family's porcelain doll collection.

Boys have their own festival on May 5. *Hamamatsu* is observed when brightly colored paper or cloth fish are flown proudly from bamboo poles in front of homes. There is a fish for each boy in the family. The fish is a symbol of courage and endurance to remind boys of the bravery shown by ancient *samurai* warriors.

The festival of *Tanabata* occurs on July 7. It is based on a legend about a weaver star-girl who fell in love with a shepherd on the banks of the Heavenly River, or Milky Way. Two bamboo reeds are set up in each house and decorated with colorful paper streamers and poems that are dropped later into a nearby river.

The Feast of the Lanterns occurs in July, and honors the spirits of dead ancestors. The Harvest Thanksgiving Festival is celebrated in October to show gratitude for bountiful harvests.

*Shichi-Go-San*, or Seven-Five-Three, is an exciting celebration on November 15. Girls who are seven, boys who are five, and all children who are three receive presents on this day. Then, the children dress in their *kimonos* and visit the shrines of their ancestors with their parents. It was believed in ancient times that the years of seven, five, and three were unlucky for children, so people prayed to their ancestors for special protection for their children of those ages.

# Festivals in Japan

## RESEARCH QUESTIONS

1. Define the following vocabulary words: *disciplined, matsuri, shrine, porridge, porcelain, endurance, shepherd,* and *bountiful.*

2. What is the entire story behind the festival of *Tanabata*? Find out and report back to the class.

3. Find out about the *Bon Festival* held in July. (*Hint:* There are fireworks involved.) Report your findings to the class.

4. Why do boys in Japan run around with deer antlers strapped to their heads in the fall? Research the *Deer-Dance Festival* and report your findings to the class.

## PROJECTS

1. In honor of New Year's, go fly a kite!

2. Make a calendar of Japanese holidays. Include a picture or symbol for each special day.

3. If you are a girl, make a doll's *kimono* for Girls' Day; if you are a boy, make a paper fish for Boys' Day.

4. What would you like to receive on Seven-Five-Three Day?

# Japanese Festivals Wordfind

```
M P A N D W H C Y K F F L O D N V C E X Z
C K V V S E O V Q G X K B U H N J M W N N
L S E K R A C N H J S B R Q D S D A D Y D
F E S T I V A L O F D O L L S X K K P W V
H V F O C E H A R V E S T F E S T I V A L
B E M I E R R N E W Y E A R S H F M T M N
E N G I P L A T F N P W V C Q Q Z O H L Y
N F M R O Q U E H T A N A B A T A N X A D
P I T J R D A R P R P H X M D D Y O D E E
P V Z V R B J N S H E P H E R D U S P Z H
G E A L I Y R F W E R E S Z Y E Y Y B B H
S T F H D H R E P E F O B B I O U Y R H O
K H L X G S C S I E I E M R B P C D L A N
C R G Z E H K T A S S F U R A P K W O G Y
Z E R T D M N I G N H S Y A J N J B V A E
K E I U V X L V L J T H Z G G Y C T U B D
X K G R T O P A Q A Z U O H Y X X H J C E
V Z G D M U N L M K X V Z P I N A F E A C
L Y U L K F S N B G C D A B L F V E J S R
```

## Can you find these words?

| | | |
|---|---|---|
| HARVEST FESTIVAL | LANTERN FESTIVAL | FESTIVAL OF DOLLS |
| SEVEN-FIVE-THREE | THREE BRANCHES | RICE PORRIDGE |
| PAPER FISH | SHEPHERD | TANABATA |
| NEW YEAR'S | KIMONOS | MATSURI |
| BOYS' DAY | WEAVER | KITES |
| JAPAN | | |

# Art and Literature

Japanese people believe that to live a truly balanced life, one must work hard but also slow down and appreciate the beauties of the world. Japanese art and literature reflect the loveliness of nature and help remind people that beauty exists only for brief moments, so one needs to stop and enjoy it while one can.

Landscapes painted on paper or silk screens are distinctly Japanese. Screen painting dates back to the 700s. Traditional Japanese homes do not have fixed walls, but use portable folding screens to divide rooms into large or small areas. Typical scenes on screens include wild animals, flowers, trees, or landscapes.

Japan is also famous for woodblock prints. In ancient times, only the wealthy could afford screen paintings, but by the seventeenth century, woodblock prints were manufactured so inexpensively in pictures and illustrated books that anyone could afford to buy them. The more popular prints showed famous actors, beautiful women dressed in ornate *kimonos*, scenes of the ocean, and national landmarks such as Mount Fuji.

The Japanese turned the crafts of lacquer and ceramics into fine art. Tea drinking became popular in the sixteenth century, and the ritual of the tea ceremony increased the production of ceramic tea sets.

The Japanese also strive for harmony with nature in architecture. Graceful pagodas with sloping roofs share space with cherry blossom trees and peaceful Japanese gardens.

The literature of Japan also reflects an appreciation of nature. Two forms of poetry created in Japan are *tanka* and *haiku*. A *tanka* poem has five lines and thirty-one syllables, while a *haiku* has three lines and seventeen syllables. Both kinds of poems deal with observations of nature.

The most famous story from ancient Japan is called *The Tale of Genju*, a long novel about life in the emperor's court in the early eleventh century. In modern times, Yasunari Kawabata from Japan won the Nobel Prize for literature in 1968.

# Art and Literature

## RESEARCH QUESTIONS

1. Define the following vocabulary words: *appreciate, literature, distinctly, portable, inexpensively, ornate, kimono, lacquer, strive, architecture, pagoda, tanka*, and *haiku*.

2. Research the process of *lacquer*. Present your findings in an informative speech using at least three visual aids.

3. What was the name of the novel that won Yasunari Kawabata the Nobel Prize for Literature in 1968? Find out.

4. Make a chart comparing a Japanese garden to a typical American garden.

5. Research the care of *bonsai trees*. Grow one and show it to the class.

## PROJECTS

1. Write either a *tanka* or *haiku* poem about a moment in nature.

2. Using resource books, draw and color a picture of a pagoda.

3. After reading about the art of Japanese flower arranging, make a flower arrangement in that style and show the class.

4. Find out the exact steps in the Japanese Tea Ceremony. Demonstrate the ceremony to the class.

5. Find examples of Japanese woodblock prints in resource books. Using pen and India ink, draw a picture in the style of Japanese woodblock prints.

# Calling All Green Thumbs!

Oh, no! The head gardener on the Grand Sushi Estate has become deathly ill from eating bad seaweed soup. He cannot draw the plans for a new rock garden on the estate. He asks you to design a pleasing garden in the space below, using shrubs, stones, and water. (He will even go so far as to allow you to use sand if you want.) Draw quickly—the master of the estate expects to see the plans in one hour!

# Music and Theater

When Japanese people have free time, they enjoy music and theater. It is estimated that fifty percent of their leisure entertainment is spent listening to music, watching concerts, and attending theater productions.

Japanese music has a distinctive sound. It features a solo voice or instrument that follows the same tune instead of blending in the Western idea of harmony. A traditional Japanese orchestra includes bamboo flutes, gongs, drums, the lute-like *biwa*, the zither-like *kota*, and the three-stringed banjo-like *samisen*. To hear what traditional Japanese music sounds like, play any minor scale on a piano.

Music plays an important role in Japanese theater as well. The oldest form of drama in Japan is the *noh* play, developed in the 1300s for the emperor and his court. It features male actors portraying both men and women, wearing elaborate silk robes and wooden masks. The main actor is center stage while the chorus and musicians sit to the side during the performance. The actors move with slow, deliberate motions as they act out an event from history or a legend. *Noh* dramas are formal and dignified, and they were the preferred theater of the emperor, the *shoguns*, and the *samurai*.

A more popular form of theater developed for ordinary audiences in the late 1500s. *Kabuki* theater is similar to *noh* in that men portray both male and female characters. However, *Kabuki* drama is different because its stories are livelier and easier to understand, and its costumes and dance movements are more exaggerated than in *noh* dramas. Also, *Kabuki* actors do not wear masks over their faces. Instead, they paint their faces with white makeup and use paint to accentuate other facial features.

Another popular form of theater in Japan is *Bunraku*, or puppet theater. The wooden puppets are quite large and require three operators: the master puppeteer controlling the head and right hand, a senior assistant working the left hand, and a junior assistant moving the body and legs. The puppeteers are dressed in black so that they are not noticed by the audience. Many *Bunraku* plays deal with war, love, and the loss of respect.

# Music and Theater

## RESEARCH QUESTIONS

1. Define the following vocabulary words: *leisure, solo, lute, zither, noh, portray, elaborate, deliberate, Kabuki, livelier, accentuate, facial, Bunraku,* and *puppeteer.*

2. Research the history of theater in Japan. Present your findings in a two-page report including at least three visual aids.

3. Find out more about the instruments in a traditional Japanese orchestra. Share your findings with the group in an oral presentation using pictures of the instruments.

4. Make a chart comparing *noh* dramas with ancient Greek theater.

## PROJECTS

1. Make your own orchestra! Construct either a *biwa, samisen,* or a drum.

2. You can play a Japanese scale by playing an A minor scale on a piano. Start on A and play all eight white keys up to the next A.

3. List similarities and differences between *noh* and *Kabuki.*

4. Make your own *Bonraku* puppet out of papier-mâché, paint, and cloth. Remember to make it large enough for three people to move the head, arms, and legs.

5. For a Western view of *Kabuki,* watch the video of Gilbert and Sullivan's *The Mikado.*

# Tokyo Entertainment Flyer

You are to design a brochure, or flyer, to inform music- and theater-goers in Tokyo what kinds of entertainment are available to them.

1. Collect all the information that you can about *noh* dramas, *Kabuki* theater, and Japanese orchestras of traditional and Western music.

2. Fold a piece of white, unlined 8½ by 11-inch paper into thirds.

3. In your neatest handwriting, print the information you have gathered about Japanese theater and music on the inside of the brochure. Remember to leave spaces after you finish writing each section so that you can draw pictures to illustrate the information.

4. Draw and color the pictures in your brochure.

5. On the front flap, write a catchy phrase about Japanese music and theater. Illustrate the front flap using color.

6. On the second flap, invite the reader to attend any of the following theater or music events, and list them.

7. Remember, you want to make your brochure appealing so that people will want to attend the events. Use a lot of color in your brochure!

# Sadako Sasaki

Sadako Sasaki's story began on August 6, 1945, when she was two years old. Japan was at war with the United States. The United States dropped the first atomic bomb in the center of Sadako's hometown of Hiroshima. The bomb destroyed three-fifths of the city, and killed over 100,000 people, either from the blast or by radiation poisoning later in their lives.

Sadako's family survived the bombing, and the Sasakis rebuilt their lives, just as the city of Hiroshima was rebuilt. Mr. Sasaki's barbershop prospered. Sadako and her older brother Masahiro soon had a baby sister named Mitsue and a baby brother named Eiji. Every day, Mr. Sasaki prayed to the spirits of his ancestors, giving thanks for his happy family and growing business, and asking for protection of his family from the radiation poisoning diseases.

Sadako grew to be an excellent runner. When Sadako was ten, she was chosen to run on the relay team to represent her school at the All-School Field Day Races. She knew that if her team won the race, she could get on the track team in junior high the following year. Sadako's team came in first, but she ran so hard that she felt dizzy and strange afterward.

The dizziness and exhaustion did not go away. When Sadako collapsed in gym class two months later, her parents took her to the Red Cross Hospital. After x-rays and blood tests were taken, the doctors confirmed that Sadako had leukemia from the atomic radiation that still lingered in the air.

Sadako's best friend, Chizuko, visited her in the hospital. Chizuko reminded Sadako of the old folktale about the crane, who is supposed to live for a thousand years. If Sadako folded a thousand cranes out of paper, the gods would make her well again. Sadako kept up her spirits by folding paper cranes. As she became weaker and the pain increased, she kept folding cranes and hoping for a miracle. She folded 644 cranes before she died on October 25, 1955. Her classmates folded 356 more cranes so that Sadako could be buried with one thousand paper cranes. Sadako Sasaki was eleven years old.

In 1958, a statue was unveiled in the Peace Park on Hiroshima. The statue is of Sadoko holding a crane in her outstretched hands. At the base of the statue are these words:

This is our cry,
This is our prayer;
Peace in the world.

# Sadako Sasaki

## RESEARCH QUESTIONS

1. Define the following vocabulary words: *atomic, radiation, survive, prosper, ancestor, leukemia, exhaustion, collapse*, and *confirm*.

2. Find out more about the city of Hiroshima. What was it like before the bomb hit it? What did the citizens do afterward? Present your findings as if you were a television reporter on a network news program.

3. Research the history of the atomic bomb and its effects. Write your findings in the form of a magazine article and include at least three visual aids.

## PROJECTS

1. Read the book, *Sadako and the Thousand Paper Cranes* by Eleanor Coerr.

2. *Origami* is the art of paper folding. Using a resource book, learn how to fold a paper crane, then demonstrate it to the class.

3. Composer David Lanz wrote a song entitled "The Crane" for the opening ceremonies of the 1990 Goodwill Games. The song was played as school children presented one thousand paper cranes to world leaders at the event. Listen to "The Crane" by David Lanz on his *Skyline Firedance* recording.

4. List ways that YOU can promote peace:
   - in your family,
   - in your school,
   - in your town,
   - in your state,
   - in your world.

# Timeline of Japan

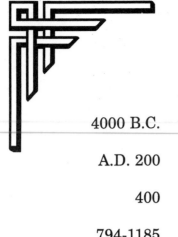

| | |
|---|---|
| 4000 B.C. | Hunter-gatherers live on the islands. |
| A.D. 200 | Japan is controlled by warring clans. |
| 400 | The Yamato clan become rulers on Kyushu. |
| 794-1185 | Golden Age of Japan |
| 1192 | Minamoto becomes first *shogun* of Japan; *Bushido,* the code of loyalty practiced by *samurai*, is written. |
| 1543 | Portuguese traders bring firearms and the influence of the outside world to Japan. |
| 1637 | All foreigners ordered to leave Japan; 200 years of isolation from rest of the world follows |
| 1853 | Commander Perry of the United States opens trade negotiations between the United States and Japan. |
| 1867 | Emperor Meiji ends rule of *shoguns* and power of *samurai;* under his direction, Japan becomes a modern, powerful country. |
| 1914–1918 | Japan fights in World War I. |
| 1941 | Japan attacks Pearl Harbor Naval Base in Hawaii; United States declares war on Japan. |
| 1945 | United States drops atomic bombs on Hiroshima and Nagasaki; Japan surrenders and World War II ends. |
| 1947 | Japan becomes a democracy. |
| 1952 | American occupation of Japan ends. |
| 1964 | Japan hosts the Summer Games of the International Olympic Games. |

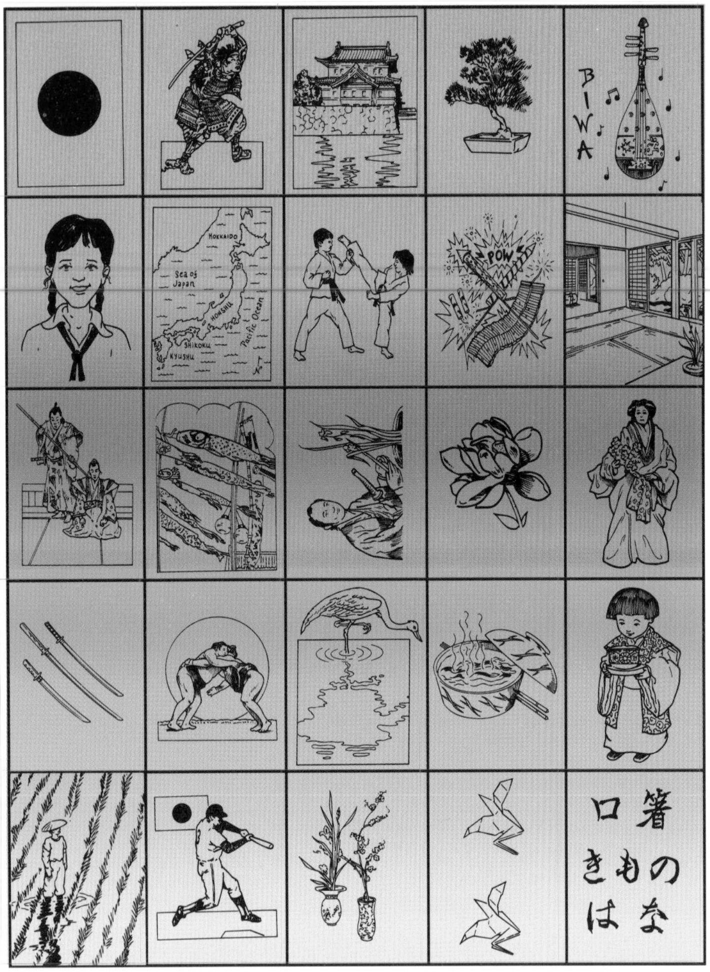
BIWA
HOKKAIDO
Sea of Japan
HONSHU
Pacific Ocean
SHIKOKU
KYUSHU
POW
口 箸
きもの
はな

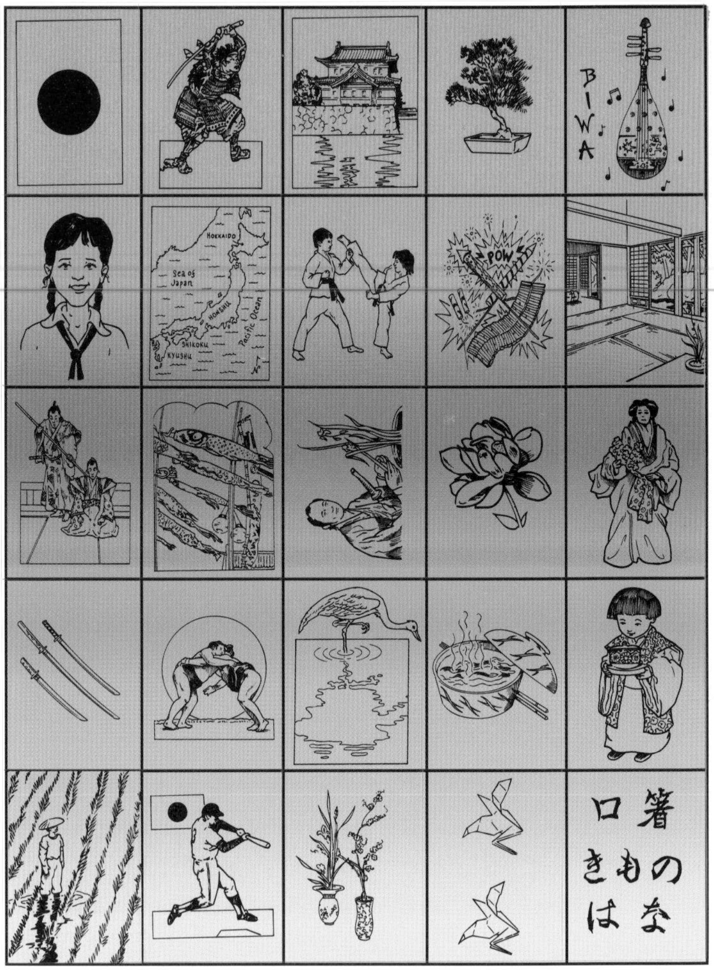
BIWA
HOKKAIDO
Sea of Japan
HONSHU
Pacific Ocean
SHIKOKU
KYUSHU
POW
口 箸
きもの
はな

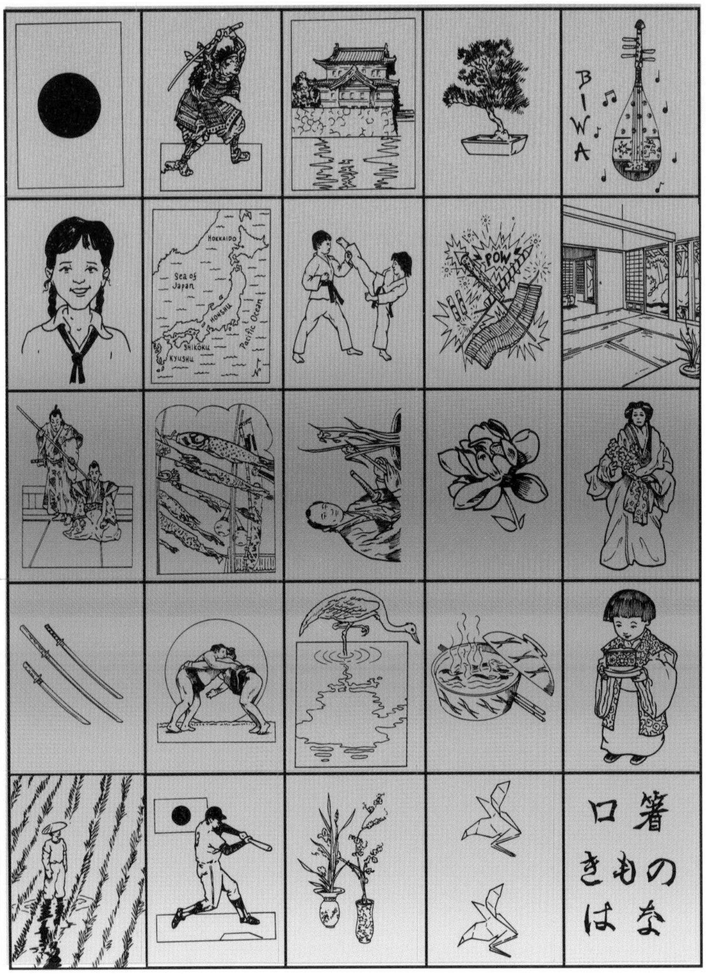
BIWA
HOKKAIDO
Sea of Japan
HONSHU
Pacific Ocean
SHIKOKU
KYUSHU
POW
口 箸
きもの
はな

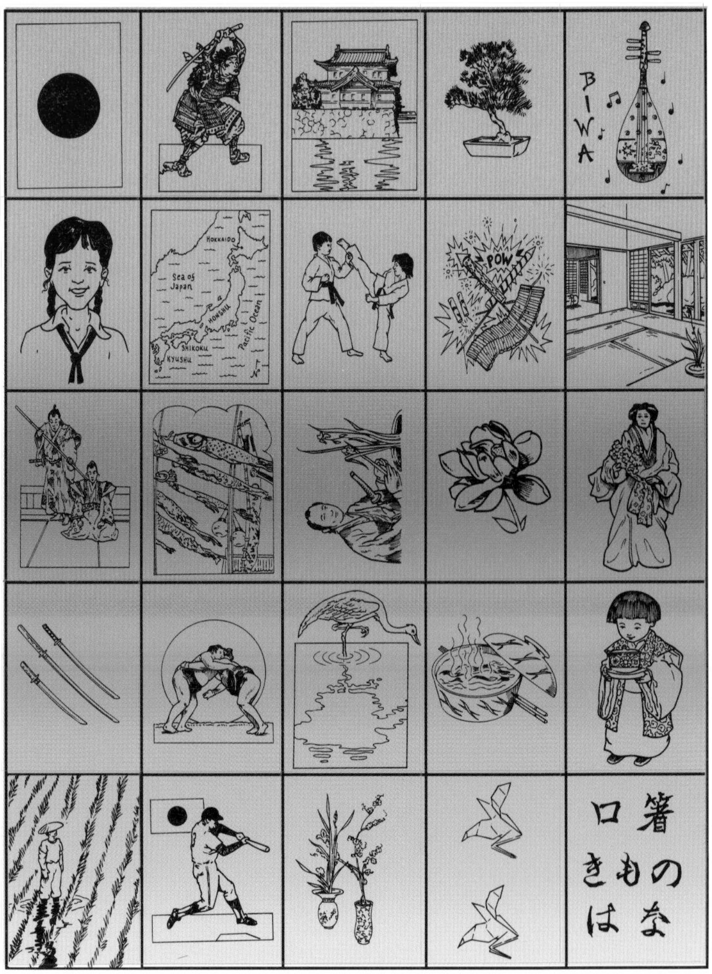
BIWA
HOKKAIDO
Sea of Japan
HONSHU
Pacific Ocean
SHIKOKU
KYUSHU
POW
口 箸
きもの
はな